SING 8 THEATRE FAVOURITES WITH A PRO

SING ALONG
SHOWTUNES

SONGBOOK & SOUND-A-LIKE CD WITH UNIQUE PITCH-CHANGER™

HAL•LEONARD

pro vocal
BETTER THAN KARAOKE!

R FEMALE SINGERS

SING 8 THEATRE FAVOURITES WITH A PROFESSIONAL BAND

SING ALONG
SHOWTUNES

SONGBOOK & SOUND-A-LIKE CD WITH UNIQUE PITCH-CHANGER™

HLE

HAL LEONARD EUROPE
Distributed by Music Sales

Exclusive Distributors:
Music Sales Limited
14-15 Berners Street, London W1T 3LJ, UK.

Order No. HLE90003793
ISBN 978-1-84938-004-1
This book © Copyright 2009 Hal Leonard Europe

Printed in the USA

Your Guarantee of Quality
As publishers, we strive to produce every book to the highest
commercial standards. The book has been carefully designed
to minimise awkward page turns and to make playing from it a
real pleasure. Throughout, the printing and binding have been
planned to ensure a sturdy, attractive publication which should
give years of enjoyment. If your copy fails to meet our high
standards, please inform us and we will gladly replace it.

www.musicsales.com

CONTENTS

Bewitched

from PAL JOEY
Words by Lorenz Hart
Music by Richard Rodgers

Intro
Ballad

He's a fool, and don't I know it,

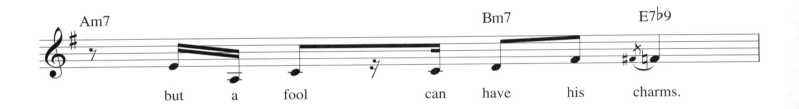

but a fool can have his charms.

I'm in love, and don't I show it, like a babe in arms.

Love's the same old sad sen-sa-tion.

Late-ly I've not slept a wink, _____

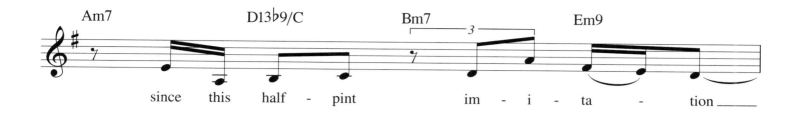

since this half - pint im - i - ta - tion ____

____ put me on the blink. ____

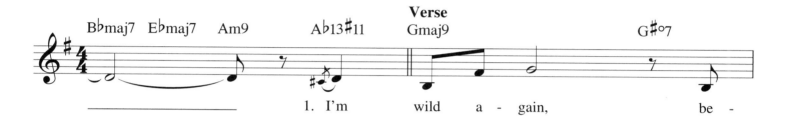

Verse

____ 1. I'm wild a - gain, be -

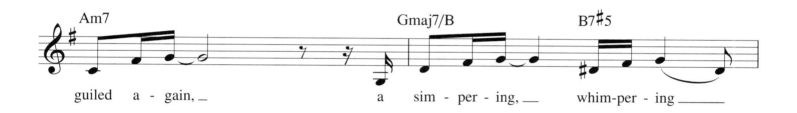

guiled a - gain, ____ a sim - per - ing, ____ whim-per - ing ____

child ____ a - gain. ____ Be - witched, both - ered and ____

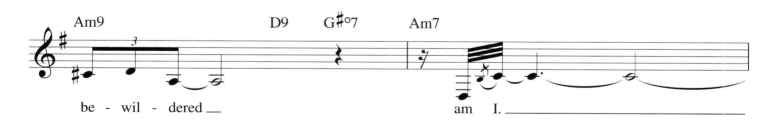

be - wil - dered ____ am I. ____

Verse

____ 2. Could - n't sleep, ____ and

7

Am7 · Bb°7 · Gmaj9/B · B7#5

would-n't sleep _____ when love _____ came and _____ told me _____ I _____

Cmaj7 · Cm9 · Gmaj9/B · Bb13

_____ should-n't sleep. _____ Be - witched, both - ered and

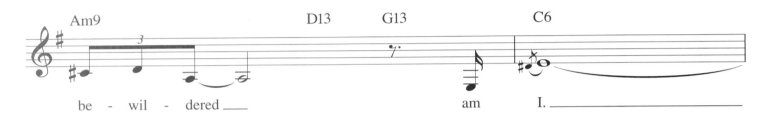

Am9 · D13 · G13 · C6

be - wil - dered _____ am I. _____

Bridge

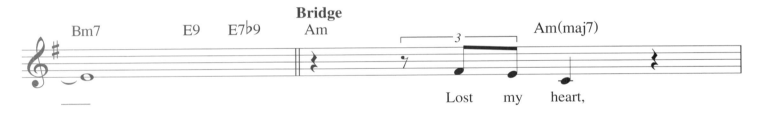

Bm7 · E9 · E7b9 · Am · Am(maj7)

_____ Lost my heart,

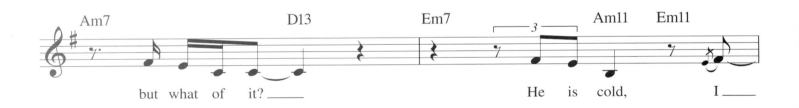

Am7 · D13 · Em7 · Am11 · Em11

but what of it? _____ He is cold, I _____

Em7 · Em6 · Am7 · Am7/G

_____ a - gree. He _____ can _____ laugh, _____ but

D7 · D7/C · Bm7 · Bb°7

I love it, al - though _____ the laugh's _____ on _____

Am9 A♭13♯11 **Verse** Gmaj9 G6

me. 3. I'll ___ sing to him, ___ each

Am7/G Gmaj9 G7♯9♭5

spring to him, and long for the day when I'll ___

Cmaj7/G Cm7/G F9/E♭ G/D B♭°7

___ cling ___ to him. ___ Be - witched, both - ered and

Am7 D7♯11♭9 Gm

be - wil - dered am I. ___

Interlude

G Cmaj7/E Gmaj9/B

Bet I'm not a new sen - sa - tion.

Cmaj7/B E9sus4 E7♭9

I've done pret - ty well, I think,

Am7 D9sus4 Gmaj7 E9sus4

but this half - pint im - i - ta - tion

put me _____ on the blink. _____

4. I've _____

Verse

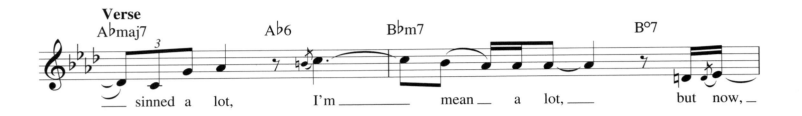

_____ sinned a lot, I'm _____ mean a lot, _____ but now, _____

_____ I'm not _____ sweet sev - en - teen a _____ lot. Be -

witched, both - ered and be - wil - dered _____

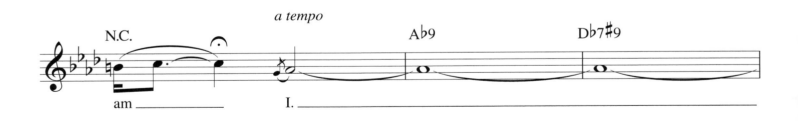

am _____ I. _____

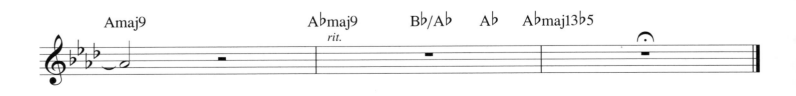

_____

Bye Bye Blackbird

from PETE KELLY'S BLUES

Lyric by Mort Dixon
Music by Ray Henderson

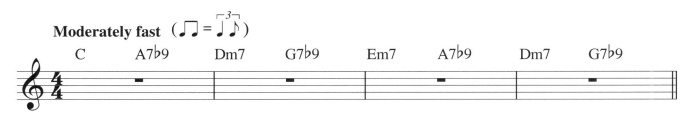

Pack up all my care and woe,   here I go

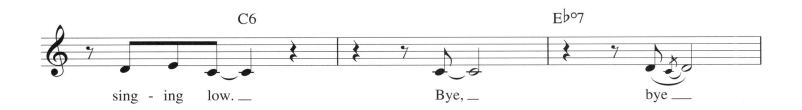

sing - ing low.   Bye,   bye

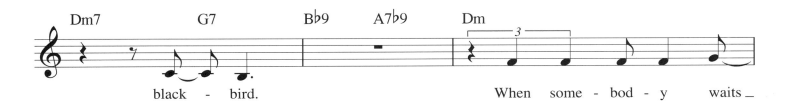

black - bird.   When some - bod - y waits

for me,   su - gar's sweet,   so is he.

Bye,   bye black - bird.

No one here could love ____ and un - der - stand ____ me. ____

Oh, what hard luck sto - ries they ____ all hand _____ me. ____

Make my bed and light ____ the light, ___ I'll ar - rive ___ a late to - night. ___ Black - bird, ___ bye, ___ bye. ___

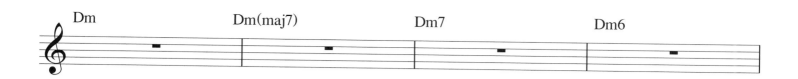

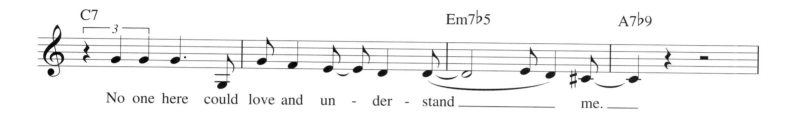

No one here could love and un - der - stand ____ me. ____

Oh, what hard luck sto - ries they all hand ____ me. ____

Make my bed and light the light, _ I'll ar - rive _ a late to - night. _

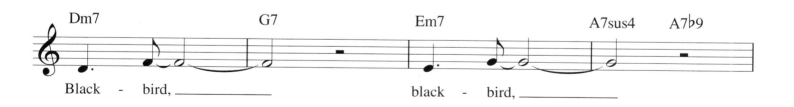

Black - bird, ____ black - bird, ____

black - bird ____ bye, ____ bye. ____

Can't Help Lovin' Dat Man

from SHOW BOAT
Lyrics by Oscar Hammerstein II
Music by Jerome Kern

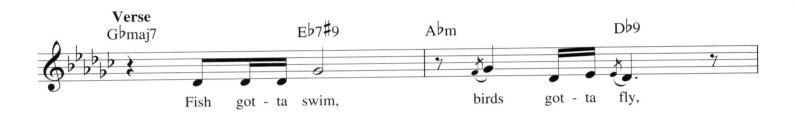

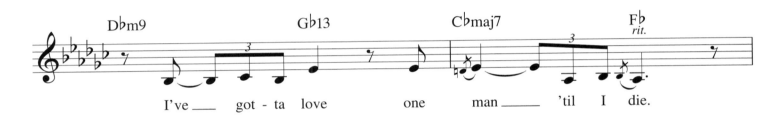

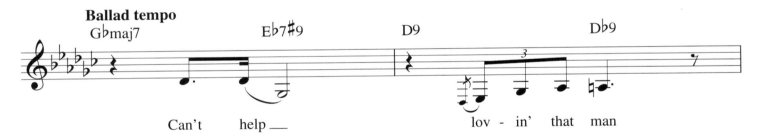

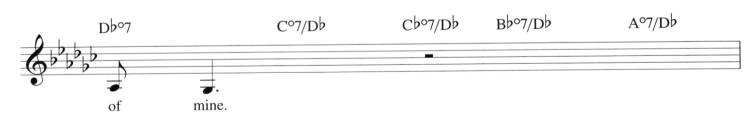

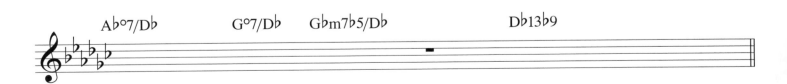

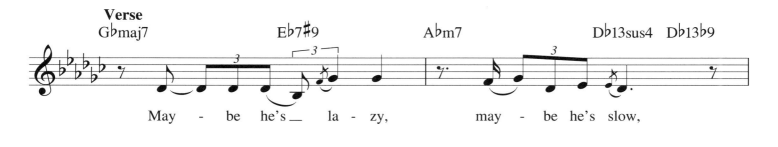

Verse

G♭maj7   E♭7♯9   A♭m7   D♭13sus4   D♭13♭9

May - be he's _ la - zy,   may - be he's slow,

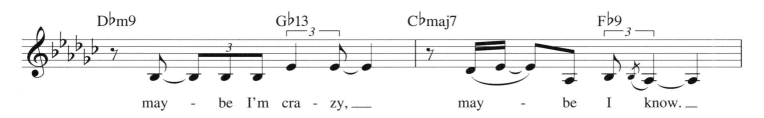

D♭m9   G♭13   C♭maj7   F♭9

may - be I'm cra - zy, _   may - be I know. _

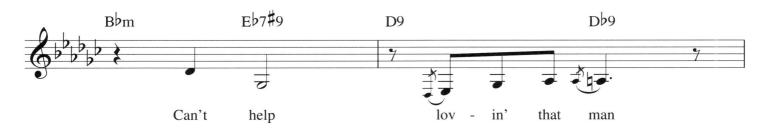

B♭m   E♭7♯9   D9   D♭9

Can't help   lov - in' that man

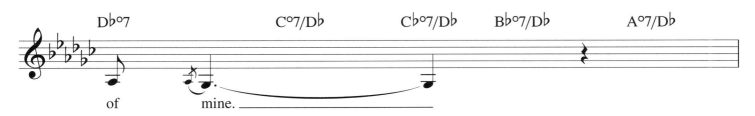

D♭°7   C°7/D♭   C♭°7/D♭   B♭°7/D♭   A°7/D♭

of   mine. _____

A♭°7/D♭   D♭13   G♭   C7♯11♭9

When _

Bridge

C♭6   C°7

he _ goes a - way,

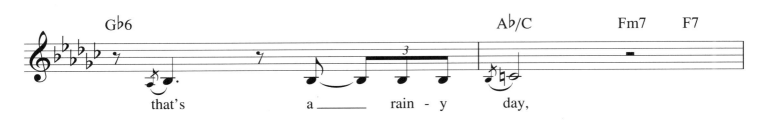

G♭6   A♭/C   Fm7   F7

that's   a ___ rain - y   day,

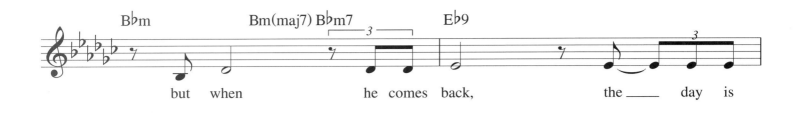

but when   he comes back,   the ___ day is

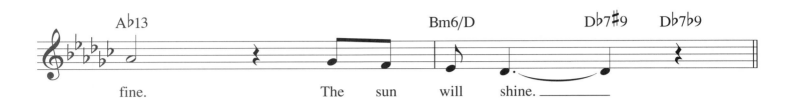

fine.   The sun will shine. ___

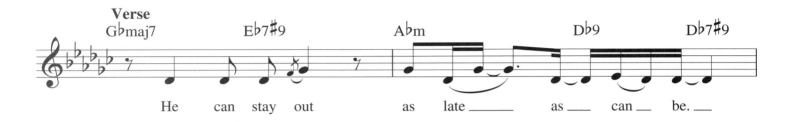

Verse

He can stay out   as late ___ as __ can __ be. __

Home __ with-out him   ain't no home __ for me. __

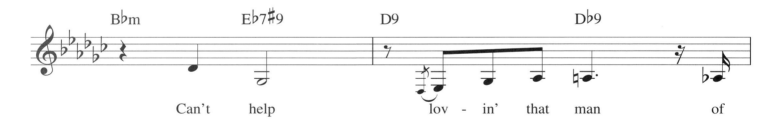

Can't help   lov - in' that man   of

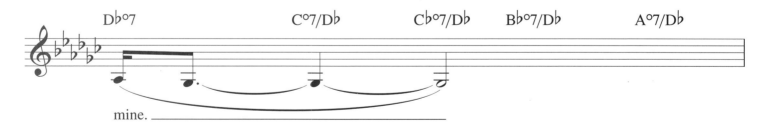

mine. ___

Bridge
Rubato (faster)

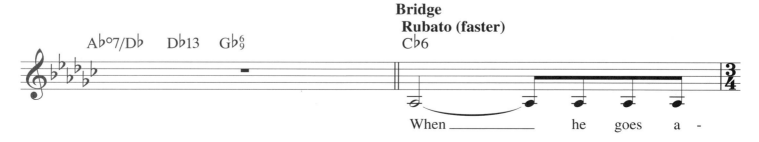

When ___ he goes a -

Don't Cry For Me, Argentina

from EVITA

Words by Tim Rice
Music by Andrew Lloyd Webber

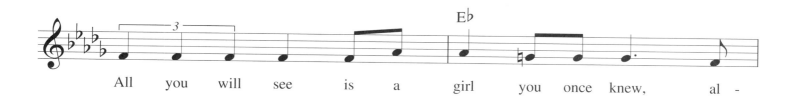

All you will see is a girl you once knew, al-

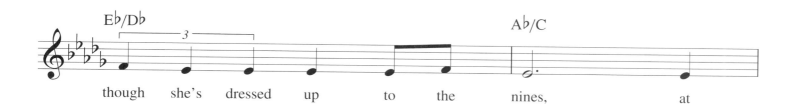

though she's dressed up to the nines, at

six - es and sev - ens with you.

Verse

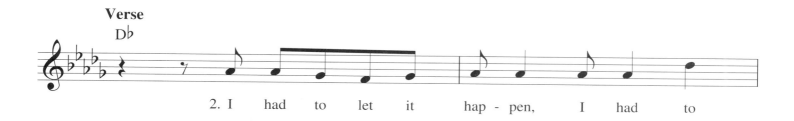

2. I had to let it hap - pen, I had to

change. Could - n't stay all my life down at

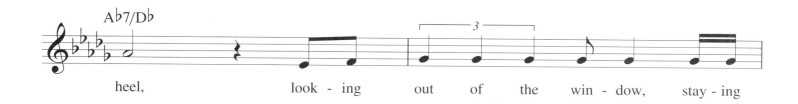

heel, look - ing out of the win - dow, stay - ing

out of the sun. So I chose free - dom,

run - ning a - round, try - ing ev - 'ry - thing new, but

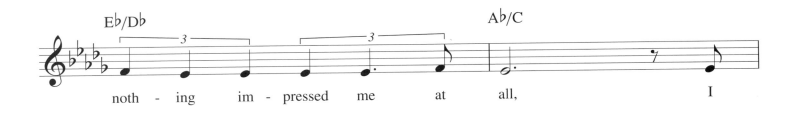

noth - ing im - pressed me at all, I

nev - er ex - pect - ed it to.

Chorus

Don't cry for me, Ar - gen - ti - na. _____ The truth is I nev - er

left you. All through my wild days, my mad ex -

is - tence, I kept my prom - ise. Don't keep your

Verse

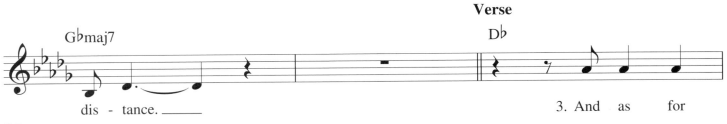

dis - tance. _____   3. And as for

for-tune, and as for fame,   I nev-er in-vit-ed them

in.   Though it seemed to the world they were

all I de-sired,   they were il-lu-sions, _ they are

not the so-lu-tions they pro-mised to be,   the

an-swer was here all the time. _____ I love you and hope you love

Chorus
Tempo I

me.   Don't cry for me, Ar-gen-ti-na.

Faster

Don't cry for me, Ar-gen-

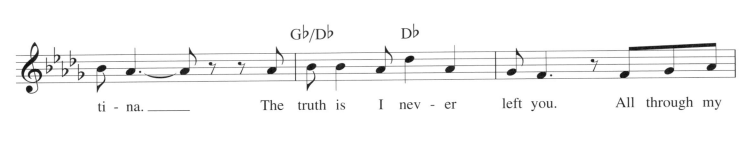

Gb/Db **Db**

ti - na. _____ The truth is I nev - er left you. All through my

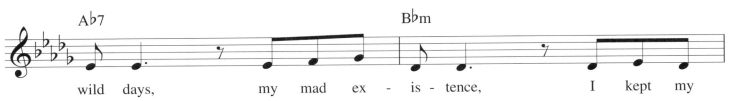

Ab7 **Bbm**

wild days, my mad ex - is - tence, I kept my

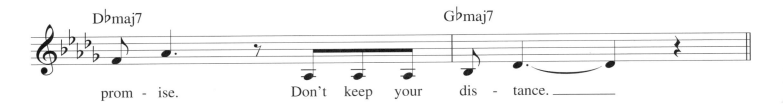

Dbmaj7 **Gbmaj7**

prom - ise. Don't keep your dis - tance. _____

Outro
Rubato

Gbmaj7

Have I said too much? There's noth - ing more I can think of to

Fm7 **Gbmaj7**

say to you. But all you have to do is

Db

look at me to know that ev - 'ry word is true.

A tempo

Gb/Db **Db** *rit.*

A tempo

Ab7 **Bbm** **Dbmaj7** **Gbmaj7**

Fly Me To The Moon

(In Other Words)

Words and Music by Bart Howard

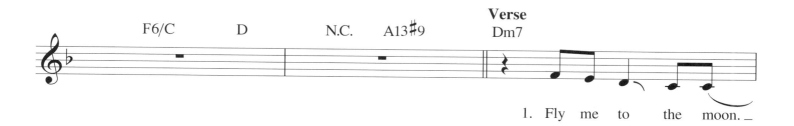

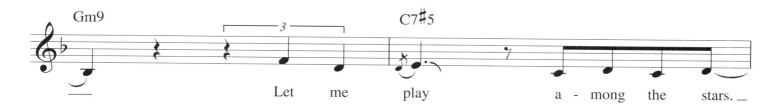

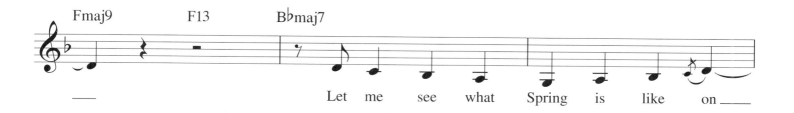

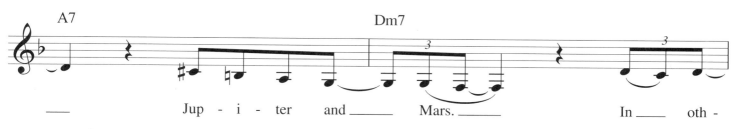

-er _____ words, ___ hold my hand. __

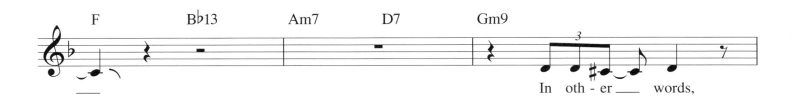
___ In oth-er ___ words,

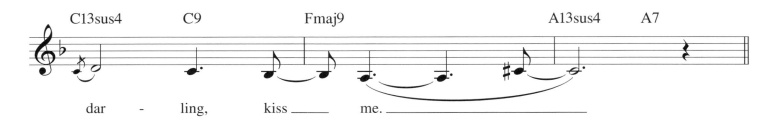
dar - ling, kiss _____ me. _____

Verse

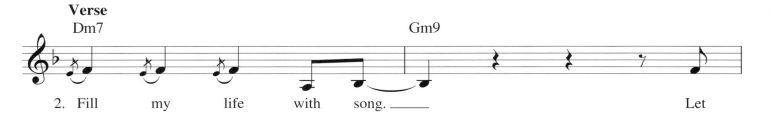
2. Fill my life with song. _____ Let

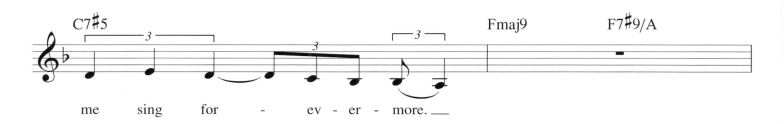
me sing for - ev - er - more. __

You are ___ all ___ I long for, all I _____

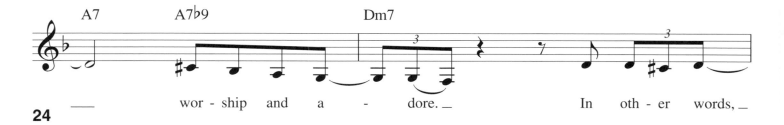
___ wor - ship and a - dore. _ In oth - er words,

24

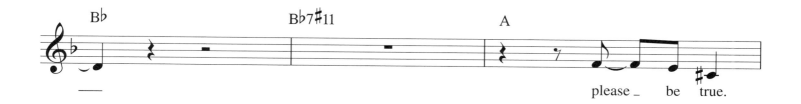

Bb   Bb7#11   A

please be true.

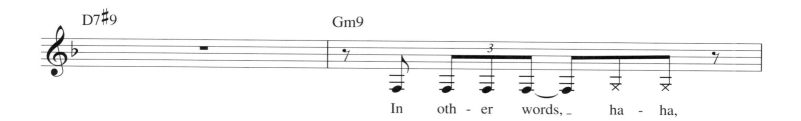

D7#9   Gm9

In oth - er words, ha - ha,

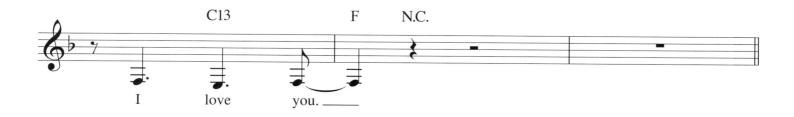

C13   F   N.C.

I love you.

Interlude

47

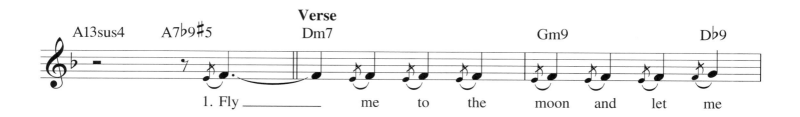

A13sus4   A7b9#5   **Verse**   Dm7   Gm9   Db9

1. Fly me to the moon and let me

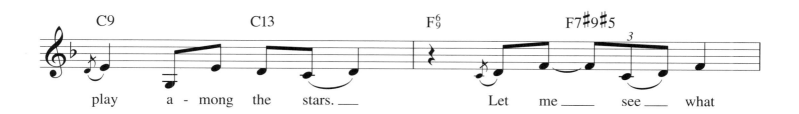

C9   C13   F6/9   F7#9#5

play a - mong the stars. Let me see what

Bbmaj13   A7

Spring is like on Jup - i - ter and

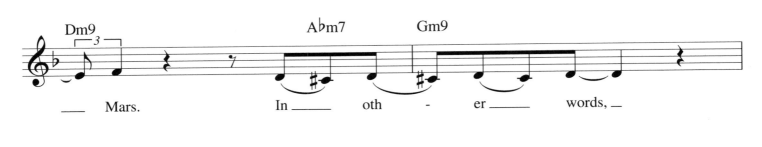

Dm9 · · · Ab m7 · Gm9
___ Mars. In ___ oth - er ___ words, ___

C7sus4 · C · C7#5 · Fmaj9 · D7b9
hold my hand. ___

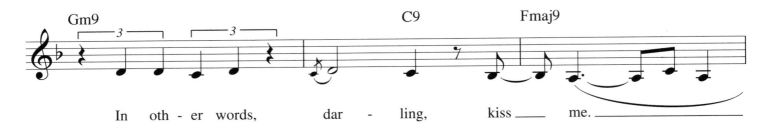

Gm9 · C9 · Fmaj9
In oth - er words, dar - ling, kiss ___ me. ___

Verse

A7#5 · Dm7 · Gm9
___ 2. Fill my life with song. ___ Let me

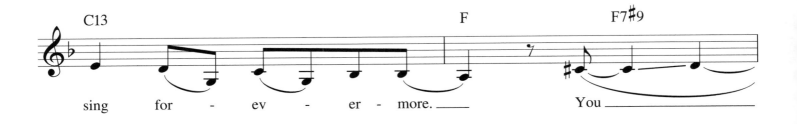

C13 · F · F7#9
sing for - ev - er - more. ___ You ___

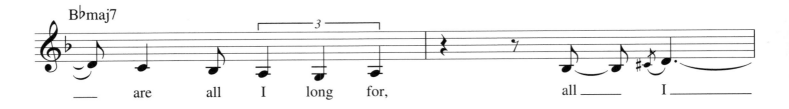

Bb maj7
___ are all I long for, all ___ I ___

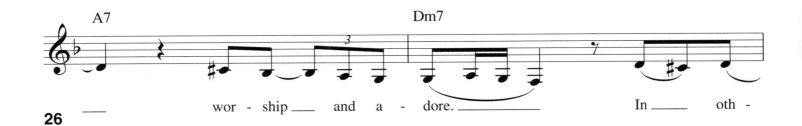

A7 · Dm7
___ wor - ship ___ and a - dore. ___ In ___ oth -

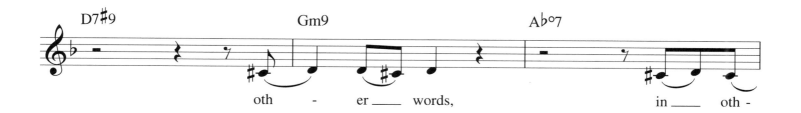

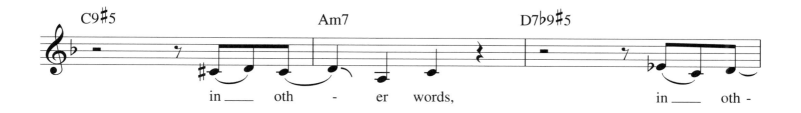

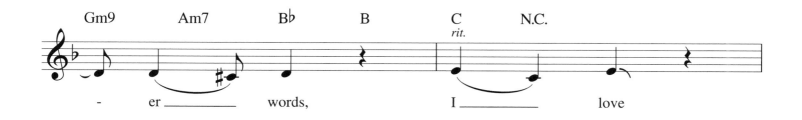

The Girl From Ipanema

(Garôta De Ipanema)

from THE COLOR OF MONEY

Music by Antonio Carlos Jobim
English Words by Norman Gimbel
Original Words by Vinicius de Moraes

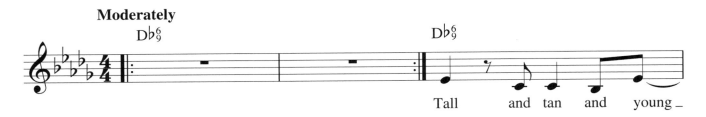

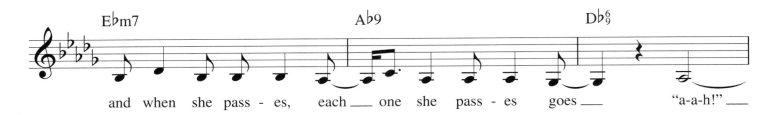

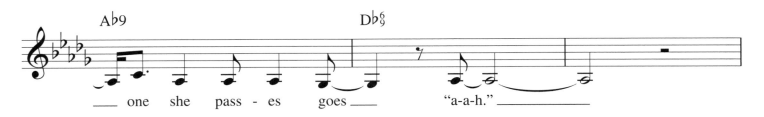

Oh, _____ but he watch - es her _____ sad - ly. _____

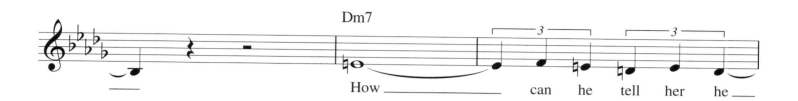

_____ How _____ can he tell her he

_____ loves her. _____ Yes, _____ he _____

_____ would give his heart glad - ly, _____ but each

day when she walks to the sea, _____ she looks straight a - head not at

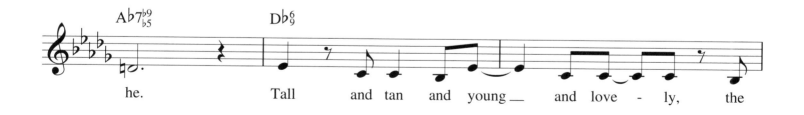

he. Tall and tan and young _____ and love - ly, the

girl from I - pa - ne - ma goes walk - in', and when she pass - es he _____

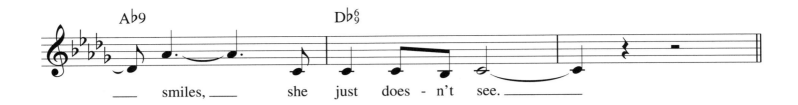

smiles, ____ she just does - n't see. ____

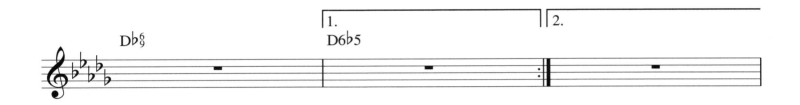

Oh, _____ but he watch - es her ____ sad - ly. ____

____ How _____ can he tell her he ___

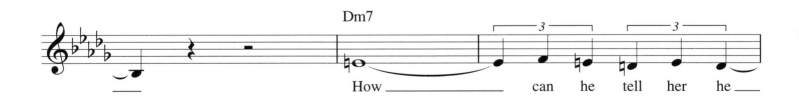

____ loves her. _____ Yes, _____ he ___

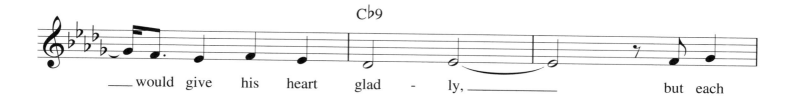

Cb9

_____ would give his heart glad - ly, _____ but each

Fm7   Bb7$^{b9}_{b5}$ Ebm7

day when she walks to the sea, _____ she looks straight a - head not at

Ab7$^{b9}_{b5}$ Db$^6_9$

he.   Tall   and tan and young ___ and love - ly, the

Eb7

girl from I - pa - ne - ma goes walk - in', and

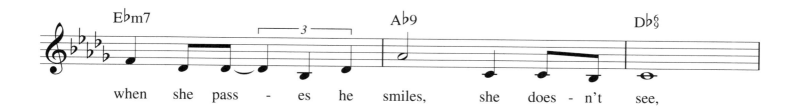

Ebm7   *3*   Ab9   Db$^6_9$

when she pass - es he smiles, she does - n't see,

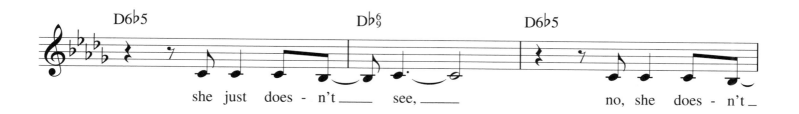

D6b5   Db$^6_9$ D6b5

she just does - n't ____ see, ____ no, she does - n't _

Db$^6_9$ D6b5   Dbmaj9
             rit.

___ see. _____   But she does - n't see.

On My Own

from LES MISÉRABLES

Music by Claude-Michel Schönberg
Lyrics by Alain Boublil, John Caird, Trevor Nunn,
Jean-Marc Natel and Herbert Kretzmer

It Never Entered My Mind

from HIGHER AND HIGHER

Words by Lorenz Hart
Music by Richard Rodgers

Intro
Ballad

Rubato

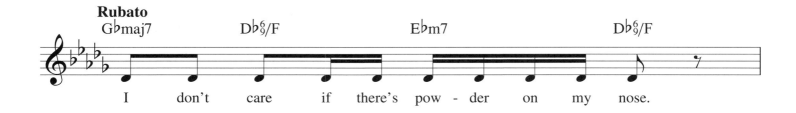

I don't care if there's pow-der on my nose.

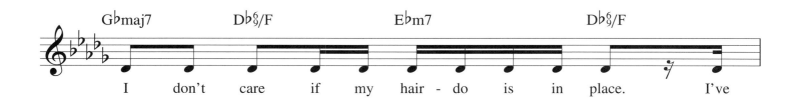

I don't care if my hair-do is in place. I've

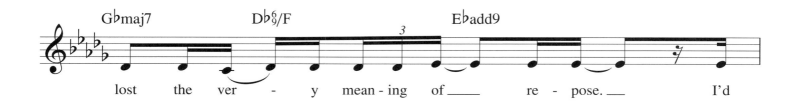

lost the ver - y mean-ing of ___ re - pose. ___ I'd

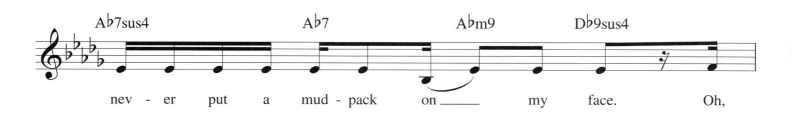

nev - er put a mud - pack on ___ my face. Oh,

who would have thought ___ that I'd walk ___ in a daze

Now I nev-er go to shows at night, but just to mat-i-nees __ now.

I see the show, __ and home I go.

Verse
Ballad

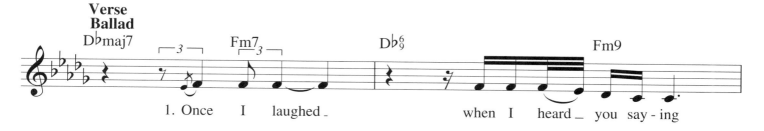

1. Once I laughed __ when I heard __ you say-ing

that I'd be play-ing ___ sol - i - taire,

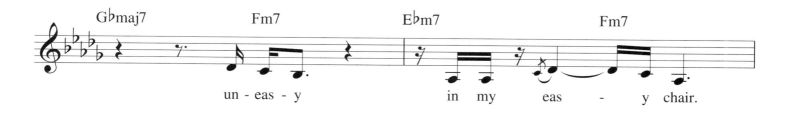

un - eas - y in my eas - y chair.

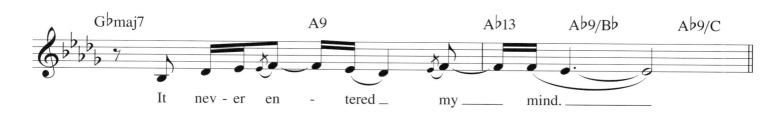

It nev-er en - tered __ my ___ mind. ___

Verse

2. Once you told __ me ___ I was mis-tak-en, ___

that I'd a-wak-en

with ____ the ____ sun ____

and or - der or - ange juice

for ____ one.

It nev-er en - tered ____ my mind. ____

Bridge

You have ____ what I lack my - self, and

now I e - ven have ____ to scratch ____ my

back ____ my - self. ____

Verse

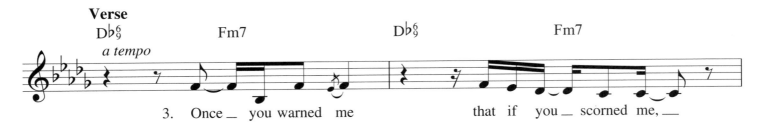

3. Once ____ you warned me that if you ____ scorned me, ____

that if you scorned me, I'd sing a maid - en's

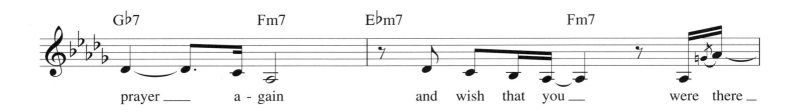

prayer ____ a - gain and wish that you ____ were there ____

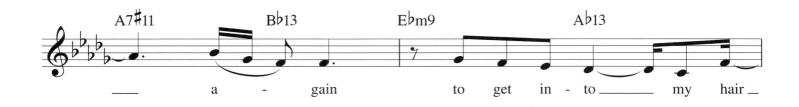

____ a - gain to get in - to _____ my hair ____

Rubato

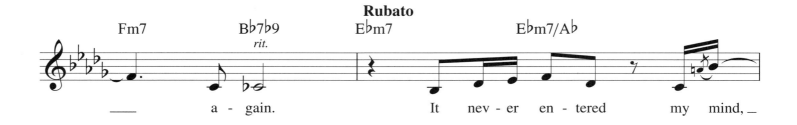

____ a - gain. It nev - er en - tered my mind, ____

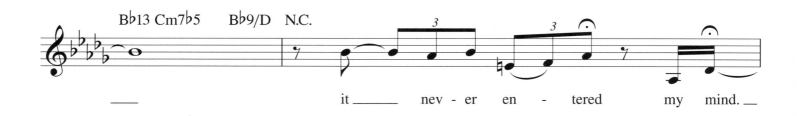

____ it _____ nev - er en - tered my mind. ____

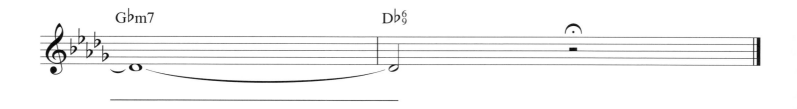